What Else Can I Pl
Flute
Grade Four

International MUSIC Publications

Series Editor: Miranda Steel

Music arranged and processed by
Barnes Music Engraving Ltd
East Sussex TN22 4HA, England

Cover design by Headline Publicity

Published 2000

DON'T BE A MUSIC COPYCAT!

The copying of © copyright material is a criminal offence and may lead to prosecution.

Introduction

In this *What Else Can I Play?* collection you'll find eighteen popular tunes that are both challenging and entertaining.

The pieces have been carefully selected and arranged to create ideal supplementary material for young flautists who are either working towards or have recently taken a Grade Four flute examination.

As the student progresses through the volume, technical demands increase and new concepts are introduced which reflect the requirements of the major examination boards. Suggestions and guidelines on tempo and dynamics are given for each piece, together with technical tips and performance notes.

Pupils will experience a wide variety of music, ranging from classical and jazz through to showtunes and popular songs, leading to a greater awareness of musical styles.

Whether it's for light relief from examination preparation, or to reinforce the understanding of new concepts, this collection will enthuse and encourage all young flautists.

Daydream believer

Words and Music by John Stewart

Try to remember

Music by Harvey Schmidt

Talk to the animals

Words and Music by Leslie Bricusse

The Pink Panther theme

Music by Henry Mancini

Close to you (they long to be)

Music by Burt Bacharach

April in Paris

Music by Vernon Duke

It's alright with me

Words and Music by Cole Porter

Coronation Street

Music by Eric Spear

Love's got a hold on my heart

Words and Music by Andrew Frampton and Pete Waterman

The greatest love of all

Music by Michael Masser

Singin' in the rain

Music by Nacio Herb Brown

Music to watch girls by

Words and Music by Anthony Verona and Sid Ramin

Toreador's song

Music by Georges Bizet

Moderate march (♩ = 118)

Star Wars (main title)

Music by John Williams

In the hall of the mountain king

Music by Grieg

I got rhythm

Music and Lyrics by George Gershwin and Ira Gershwin

Mexican hat dance

Traditional

In the mood

Music by Joe Garland

Why not extend your repertoire with:

Congratulations! You've Just Passed Grade 1

6796A
Alto Saxophone

6797A
Clarinet

6794A
Flute

6798A
Piano

6795A
Violin

- Features standard repertoire which is ideal for Grades 1-2.

- Available for clarinet, alto saxophone, flute and violin with piano accompaniment; and piano solo.

- A wide variety of titles from jazz to pop, and from classical to folk.

- Fifteen great progressive titles in each book.

Series includes: *Angels – Autumn Leaves – Blueberry Hill – Bye Bye Blackbird – Don't Bring Lu Lu – The Hippopotamus Song – How Do I Live – I Don't Want To Miss A Thing – I'm Forever Blowing Bubbles – I've Got No Strings – Jeepers Creepers – My Heart Will Go On*